KT-472-667

For Alex *A.S.*
To Richard *C.H.*

Oxford University Press, Great Clarendon Street, Oxford OX2 6DP

Oxford is a trade mark of Oxford University Press

First published 1999

Andrea Shavick and Charlotte Hard have asserted their moral right to be known as the authors of the work.

A CIP catalogue record for this book is available from the British Library

ISBN 0 19 279022 6(hardback)
ISBN 0 19 272344 8(paperback)

Printed in Hong Kong

The Truth About Babies

Andrea Shavick

Illustrated by Charlotte Hard

Oxford University Press

Growing babies

When ladies have babies they get fat!
It takes a long time to grow a baby.

Your mum will get tired. It's hard work for her carrying a baby around inside her tummy. She'll need help.

You'll have to help make supper, tidy up, fetch and carry, in fact all the things you've never helped her with before. All the time.

'It's not fair!'

And baby comes too!

But wait a minute. Everywhere your mum goes, the baby goes too. That means that your new brother or sister takes you to school. The baby hears your name and what your voice sounds like.

Everyone will say the same thing over and over again.

It will drive you mad.

Getting ready

In the hospital they have a machine that lets you see inside your mum's tummy.

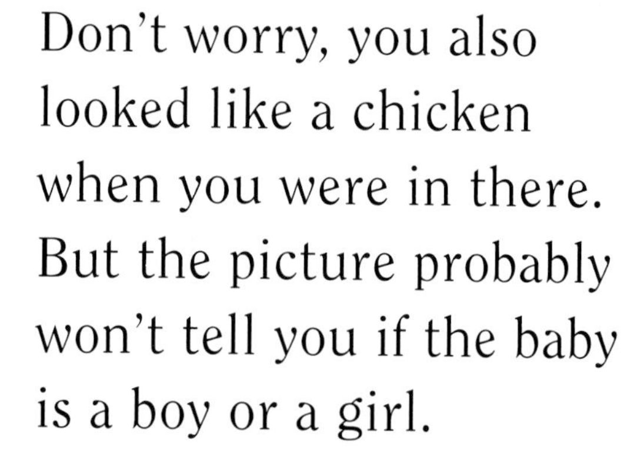

Don't worry, you also looked like a chicken when you were in there. But the picture probably won't tell you if the baby is a boy or a girl.

The first thing your mum did when you were born was look at your bottom! – to see if you were a boy or a girl.

Babies are only little, but they take up a lot of room. They need a lot of stuff. Some of it will be *your* old things.

'That's mine!'

Nobody knows when the baby...

Nobody knows exactly when the baby will be born, but there is one way you can tell. Your mum will start behaving strangely.

Suddenly she won't be tired any more.

She'll tidy up.
She'll even tidy up your things without yelling at you.

Someone else will look after you when your mum is having the baby.
You and your mum can both have a suitcase ready by the front door.

The new baby

Are new babies cute, cuddly and adorable?

No, they are not. All new babies are hideous.

Yours will be bright red, with blotches all over.

It will cry all the time.

If you think that was bad, wait until it comes home.
New babies only do four things . . .

Drink milk

Sick it up again

Cry and scream

and smell!

Milk

Some babies drink milk from a bottle. But your mum may feed the baby herself. This is called breast-feeding.

Your mum will sit for *hours* feeding the baby.

Noise

At night, you'll be fast asleep in bed when . . .

A baby crying is louder than a jumbo jet taking off.
You could try this. Get an alarm clock, set the alarm for lunch time, and put it underneath the cot.

Your baby is put to bed for a nap. The alarm will go off and baby will wake up and scream and won't go to sleep again. None of this matters because you'll be at school. By the time *you* go to bed it will be too exhausted to cry. But whatever you do . . . don't tell your mum.

She won't be pleased that you've found a way of making the baby sleep all night.
Whatever they say, grown-ups like getting up in the middle of the night to play with babies!

Nappies
'Ahhh! Mum!'
Babies' bottoms are so smelly they need to wear nappies for about two years!

One of your jobs will be to tell your mum when your baby needs a new nappy.

That's another funny thing about grown-ups, they never seem to notice the smell. Perhaps they like it!

Sick

Babies are sick on everything. All the time.
You and your mum might be sitting down together
reading a book and she's holding the baby.
All nice and cosy.
What's that funny noise like water
going down the plug?

Glug glug glug

glug glug

g l u g

Oh no!

When you go out no one will talk to you. No one will talk to your mum either.

All they want to do is goggle at the new baby and make silly faces, and go ‘goo goo.’

But wait . . . your brother or sister will get bigger, and people will notice you again instead of just sticking their bottoms up in the air!

On the move!

Your baby will get fed up with being little.
Your baby will want to be big like you.
You don't sit in a high chair, do you?
Your baby won't want to, either.

You don't sleep in a cot, do you?
Your baby won't want to sleep
in a cot, either.

You don't crawl, do you?
Watch out, because very
soon your baby will be able to
run as fast as you.

Or even faster.

Reach your toys.

Turn the TV off whenever
you want to watch.

Scribble on your books.

Eat your supper.

Steal your favourite teddy, and push you over when you try to get it back.

And when something gets broken,
or you have an argument,
you'll get the blame.
The big one always does.

When you go to school

But when you go to school
you'll both miss each other.

And when you come home again, somebody
will show you where Mum's hidden the biscuits.

That's when you'll realize that your sicky, stinky-bottomed cry-baby has turned into somebody you can really love.